old wives' tales:
remedies, pills and potions

carol cooke

© Carol Cooke

ISBN 1 901888 32 0

First published 2002

Cover Design Dominic Edmunds
Illustrations including Cover Illustration by Sheila Graber

Published in Great Britain by
Business Education Publishers Limited
The Solar Building
Doxford International
Sunderland
SR3 3XW

Tel: 0191 5252410
Fax: 0191 5201815

British Cataloguing-in-Publications Data
A catalogue record for this book is available from the British Library

Printed in Great Britain by Athenaeum Press, Gateshead.

Content

To my mother, Lilian Bianchi, who remembered a little and laughed a lot.

Introduction

I love hearing unlikely tales and believe me, there are none more unlikely than the ways in which people used to guard against infection, or, if they succumbed, fight it off. The thread that runs through all of these remedies, pills and potions, is the belief that the human body is, by and large, a lot more robust than we often imagine. We are capable of withstanding the most stringent medicines and outlandish cures, for the sake of pursuing the holy grail of good health. Barring work-related accidents and work-induced diseases, people of past generations survived against the odds and sometimes even flourished.

Work related accidents and diseases, coupled with not having two pennies to rub together, accounted for much of our grandparents' health problems. In many cases our fathers and grandfathers were forced to work in hostile and unpleasant environments. My great grandfather for example, was a diver and worked underwater, building the pier at South Shields, my grandfather worked down the pit as an overseer, and my husband's father worked in a metal foundry, with all of the attendant dangers of fire and chemical accidents.

My great grandmother meanwhile, had to raise seven children on very little money. Her husband, good money but also knew how to spend it in the many pubs, which dotted the way home. My grandmother had to cope with my coalminer grandfather who almost died when a fuse blew up in his face down the pit, and my husband's mother kept the household together while working part-time at Wright's Biscuit Factory, where the girls were tough, but you could have a laugh and share tips on how to survive.

Survival was, and remains, the name of the game. Today we rush about, and our lives often appear to be on the verge of chaos, as we juggle family, work, home, friends and health. We tend to think back longingly to a golden age of order, where there was a place for everything and everything was in its place, and you knew who to turn to in times of trouble and disaster. Mothers had a ready answer for health problems and grannies could always be counted on to know the best way of dealing with a child who had colic or a persistent cough which just wouldn't go away. But I don't know if this sort of order ever really existed. Look at this cry of exasperation:

> we sometimes wish that home life in the present day could be more like what it used to be in the days of our grandmothers. Then the whole machinery of the household seems to have worked smoothly and if anything went wrong the culprit was blamed.

You might think that this was written last week, or last month or last year, bemoaning the fact that 'fings ain't what they used to be', to quote Lionel Bart. However, this little mew of distress was written and published on June 28 1881 in a magazine full of handy hints called *The Christian Way*. I found the piece on the back of a recipe for Scotch shortbread. It had been cut out of the magazine and stored in a handwritten book of remedies and receipts, by Jane Catherine Barnsley who started her recipe and remedy book on 8 January 1850.

Jane was sorry that things were not as they were in her grandparents time, which would probably be around the 1800s, but I'm not. I'm glad, because reading through some old books of remedies for coughs, colds, influenza and the like, I'm amazed that anyone lived to celebrate their twenty-first birthday. In days gone by we were blithely instructed to drink poison, have X-rays at the drop of a hat, and anoint ourselves with neat lead!

Coupled with this rigorous, fool-hardy and some would argue downright suicidal attitude to health and well being, are some old wives tales and potions which have their roots in a solid, if instinctive knowledge of how to heal ones body using what was to hand.

I don't know about you, but as I get older I find that by and large, I can tell when I'm going to be ill, and know roughly how to treat whatever it is I've got. I tend to phone the doctor and order up the same remedy, but now and then, I ask my mother's advice and am amazed with some of the odd stories and suggestions she comes up with. And she's not living in a twilight world, but logs on to the Internet regularly, and has even been known to help my niece with designing a web page. She and her friends do remember some funny tales about health, and old fashioned remedies though. They make me laugh, and I hope they entertain you.

Ears and how to deal with them

Hot solutions

In the past our fairly namby pamby attitudes to health would have been laughed to scorn. Ears, which are now regarded as rather delicate – we are told not to put anything larger than an elbow into an ear – were regularly poked and prodded and subjected to horrid torture, all in the name of good health.

People don't seem to be laid low now with earache but two friends of mine, from different parts of the country, both confessed to suffering from the most raging earaches. The remedies could be seen as a little bizarre by today's standards, but did give instant relief.

Yon Lawson, a friend living in South Shields, remembers the agony of awful earache as a child. The pain was terrific and would only be assuaged when her mother heated up an onion in the oven, wrapped it in a cloth, put it in a scarf and tied the whole lot round her head. My other ear achy friend, Marlene Ayre, who lives in America but came from Manchester, says that she too suffered from earache, which could only be assuaged by – wait for it, and watch for regional differences – a potato, baked in the oven, wrapped in a cloth, put in a scarf and tied round her head. They must have looked like something out of *The Broons* cartoon.

Well I've heard of "Cauliflower Ear" but…

Yon always thought that the onion contained medicinal properties, but on reflection, it was most likely the heat, which helped ease the pain.

Marlene now wonders how she did not sustain a burst eardrum, what with all of that infection coupled with intense heat – but in fact the remedy worked a treat.

I mentioned these hot vegetable solutions, in a rather bemused way, to my husband. He said that this was nothing new to him. His mother too had used the properties of heat to solve earache, which always, for some reason, started at night, just before my husband was due to go to bed. He said his mother had used warm olive oil and a hot water bottle. She heated the oil and poured it into the offending ear, then filled a hot water bottle and made my husband hold the hot water bottle up against his ear. 'That must have been nice,' I said, 'Comforting,…you know,… the heat on your sore ear.' His face assured me that this wasn't the case. He said, 'it was agony. The hot water bottle used to burn, so that as well as earache you also had burns to the side of your face and ear, but the pain did ease and I got to sleep eventually'.

I guess some remedies work, and others are just a pain in the ear.

A bit of medical advice

Medical books published at the time show a similarly robust attitude to health. *Everybody's Family Doctor*, written in

Harley Street W1, published by Odhams Press Ltd, recommends this alarming course of action:

> an ear should not be allowed to discharge for more than a month without having a serious talk with a doctor on the advisability of having an operation to stop the discharge ...which may in time even give rise to a brain abscess.

Blimey, they were fairly relaxed about health advice in those days. Earache, which they suspected could lead to trouble with your brain should not be suffered for longer than a month. Today, we wouldn't suffer it for longer than five minutes!

Almond oil and the porous bone

Another friend, Anne, said that when she and her sisters were children in the 1960s, her mother Maureen Garrett used to treat their earache with almond oil, rubbed behind their ears. The reasoning behind this was that Maureen had taken notice of *Everybody's Family Doctor* and his ears and elbows talk. Anne says she still can't figure out what good it did, because the only thing behind your ears is skull and even almond oil would have difficulty seeping through skull to get to the inner ear. However it was comforting and cosy and if asked, Anne still gives the same advice as her mother – almond oil, rubbed behind the sore ear.

Today aromatherapists still recommend using almond oil combined with lavender oil, for earache and earwax build up, although they normally advocate soaking a piece of cotton wool with the remedy and inserting it into the ear.

Obvious clues

In the past, children in particular, seemed to wear their illnesses with pride. There was little attempt to spare anyone the gory details, and every attempt to draw attention to the problem. I remember countless friends in my class at school arriving with one of their ears bunged up with a piece of grubby cotton wool. The cotton wool was always grubby because children couldn't resist taking it out, inspecting it to see how things were getting on in there, and re-inserting it. This process would happen at least once every hour, and twice during playtime. Well, you had to do something, there were no climbing frames or bays painted on the playground. We had to make our own amusement.

People who suffered from earache often had to have wax removed so that they could hear again and the only way for this to be managed successfully was via a very messy and greasy process. Olive oil was warmed and then dropped into the ear in an attempt to soften the wax. The cotton wool was therefore a rough attempt at devising a home-made plug, to prevent oil and wax pouring out of the ear at inopportune moments and in fact is still used

Today, ears are syringed and wax successfully removed by aiming a jet of water towards the roof of the ear canal. However, olive oil is still recommended to soften the wax before this process is carried out.

Ear excavations

In the case of severe earache doctors would, of course, be consulted. However, if the problem presented itself as simply a raging pain without any further complications, then a sort of do-it-yourself attitude would often prevail. People would attempt to remove wax from children's ears with any implement which came to hand.

I remember being rather delicate as a child (the doctor told my mother to wrap me in cotton wool and feed me brandy when I was born) and I suffered the most terrible earache. This was treated by sitting me by the fire while my father wrapped a piece of cotton wool round the top of a match and then poked away in my ears until wax was dislodged. Not very scientific but it seemed to do the trick. Warmth and close contact with your mam or dad worked better than most medicines and had added benefits of making you feel loved.

Toothache

Hell's teeth

We're rather proud of our teeth today. We go to inordinate lengths to keep them, and are even reaching the American tooth standard which declares that every child should have a brace. We whiten our teeth, use special toothpaste which causes the gums to gleam bright pink, and are never tired of flossing, cleaning, mouth washing, chewing gum to prevent bad breath, and spraying freshener to dispel any lingering traces of the garlic we ate last night. In short, keeping our teeth and mouth fresh is almost a full-time occupation. The aisles of our supermarkets are crammed with products designed for our mouths. But it wasn't always so.

Dentifrice – pink or green?

Can you remember Dentifrice? I thought so. We all remember Dentifrice because at one time it was the only thing there was between you and soot to clean your teeth. Dentifrice was made by Gibbs and came in a little tin. Inside the tin was a block of some sort of powdery substance. I remember it being pink but my pal Heather Morgan swears it was green. Pink sounds more appealing to me. After all, you'd want your gums to look pink wouldn't you, rather than green? However, you wouldn't necessarily want your teeth to look bright pink, so I wouldn't be prepared to swear to the colour. You swirled your toothbrush around the block of powdery substance until you had a nice gooey mess, which you'd transfer to your mouth and brush away.

Catherine Ford remembers someone telling her a handy little tip. If you didn't want to go to all the expense of buying Dentifrice, you could brush your teeth with a special type of chalk that people used to clean piano keys. This chalk acted like toothpaste but cost half the price and rejoices under the name of Camphorated Chalk for Keys.

Soot and salt

Heather Morgan's dad told her that she could clean her teeth with a mixture of soot and salt. Mr Morgan had been a prisoner of war during World War II and said that he had used the soot and salt method in the camps.

Soot and salt is mentioned by everyone old enough to know how it was BT (Before Toothpaste). Indeed, as far back as the 16th Century, the preferred method of tooth cleaning was a clean cloth dipped in salt or soot, perfumed with watered pumice and rubbed on the teeth in order to polish them; salt whitens the teeth, helps remove plaque and is healthy for the gums. So not a bad alternative to Dentifrice after all.

Advert for Gibbs Dentifrice 1943

Alcohol

Whatever was wrong with you, someone somewhere would always have a remedy involving alcohol. As well as using alcohol as an antiseptic and a solution to the misery of coughs and colds, people also used alcohol as a sure-fire remedy for the pain of toothache.

Audrey Anne Myers says her mother used to recommend soaking cotton wool in whiskey and then placing it on a sore or damaged tooth. Presumably the recipient was so grateful for the gradual release of whiskey, that they forgot about their toothache and were able to blithely function all day long.

It sounds good, and worked a treat, at least until the next time, but can you imagine a posse of small children marching to school smelling of whiskey!

An interesting theory

Some time ago I visited the dentist and while I was lying prostrate with my mouth full of ironmongery, the dentist chose to expound his theory of teeth. He reckons that my mother's age group used to be forced to have their teeth out fairly rapidly, because of gum infection and tooth decay. Such major extracting can be avoided altogether today because of the advances we have made in the treatment of gum infections like pyorrhoea and gingivitis.

A friend, Joyce Telford says that she had gingivitis and her dentist simply cut off a strip of her gum at the front of her mouth. The dentist's receptionist fainted at the sight of all of the blood flowing from Joyce's butchered mouth and Joyce says she was forced to walk over a mile home, because she thought that if she attempted to get on a bus she would frighten the bus driver and the passengers.

My dentist said that my generation's mouths were filled with various bits of fillings and emergency dentistry, designed to stop us having to have all of our teeth removed, while our children's teeth are subjected to preventative measures and so should need very little in the way of fillings or extractions.

I wouldn't be inclined to disagree with my dentist, especially while sitting in the dentists chair, but that aside, I found the theory very interesting.

The effects of the War on teeth

Children who grew up during the war seem to have been blessed with good teeth, largely due to the fact that anything you liked was rationed. Sweets were obviously severely rationed. People would take their ration books to the grocer and each adult would be eligible for 8 oz. (227 gm) of sugar a week.

Not content with this appalling level of sugar deprivation, in · July 1940 the government decided to put a complete ban on the making or selling of iced cakes, and in September of the same year, also put a stop to the manufacture of 'candied peel' or 'crystallised cherries'. This meant that traditional wedding cakes disappeared for some time. As a consequence, sugar and sweets were regarded as luxuries which were difficult to obtain and so became infinitely desirable.

However, people are ingenious at getting round problems and have always displayed initiative, cunning and daring in getting what they want when they want it, in this case, sweets. Beryl Henderson remembers collecting sugar coupons and taking them over to Welch's Toffee Factory in North Shields. They would exchange your sugar coupons for delicious toffees with no questions asked.

The versatility of cloves

According to Bill Hearn, you always knew if someone was suffering from toothache because they smelled of oil of cloves. My sister's husband, Les Phillips remembers his mother giving him cloves to put on his teeth if he complained of toothache. He says, 'it worked but it was horrible. It had a disgusting taste and burned your tongue'. However clove oil is a time-honoured remedy for toothache as it is highly antiseptic and highly effective as a pain killer.

A friend called Eddie MacNamee was once given a Do-It-Yourself Emergency Dental Kit, in case he was lost in the desert and needed to do a bit of emergency root canal repair work, and guess what the kit contained – you've got it – cloves!

Cloves seem to have been very versatile because Les Phillips also remembers that his mum had a pot of cloves which were used in cases of earache. The cloves would be gently heated in olive oil, strained and placed into the ear using some kind of dropper.

Madness

In the past people seem to have been driven mad by toothache. Well they must have been mustn't they, how else could you account for the barbaric methods used to remove teeth. Les Phillips can actually remember wrapping cotton round a bad tooth which had been giving him gyp, then tying the cotton to a door handle and slamming the door. The cotton tugged at the tooth and removed it, after a considerable amount of slamming and retying of cotton. He adds, "my teeth have colossal roots, its always a problem with the dentist'.

On the subject of do-it-yourself

You may be the most confident amateur doctor, full of up-to-date knowledge about all things medical, and quietly confident that you can diagnose and indeed treat, if only the law allowed, all of your friends' aches and pains. However, even the most confident of people would perhaps baulk at filling bad teeth.

A few drops of whiskey and I'm completely legless and toothless!

A little tome belonging to Catherine Ford of South Shields, called *Enquire within upon Everything*, knows it all. As the title suggests, it is a weighty and self confident manual, full of good advice to householders, published at the turn of the century by Houlston and Sons of Paternoster Square, London, and has the definitive answer. The self help volume outlines a very conservative method for curing toothache, involving, 'two or three drops of essential oil of cloves on a small piece of lint placed in the hollow of the tooth'.

Flushed with success at this short sharp cure, the book then goes on, without so much as an indrawn breath at its own daring, to explain how you can fill your own or other people's teeth. There is no hesitation expressed at all. It sounds like something in a long list of jobs that our grandparents may have contemplated at the start of the day. You can imagine the sort of thing – bake bread, buy vegetables, black lead the fireplace, starch aprons, fill teeth. Sounds familiar? No? Thank goodness. We must assume then that people took what they read in *Enquire within upon Everything* with a pinch of salt. Anyway, I'll repeat the alarming set of instructions, just in case anyone has an old silver thimble they don't use anymore.

We start in a fairly relaxed way with something called 'Gutta Percha Toothstopping', which goes like this:

> since the introduction of gutta percha, the use of
> metallic succedaneum for filling decayed teeth has
> been superseded, especially in cases where the cavities
> are large. The gutta percha is inodorous, cheap, and

can be renewed as often as required. It is only necessary to soften it by warmth, either by holding it before a fire or immersing it in boiling water. Succedaneum is best when the decayed spots are very small.

This all seems very cosy. People at home, warming Gutta Percha, before using it to plug cavities in their teeth. But think again, this is dentistry on a major scale, without access to any form of pain control. Not so cosy after all.

We move quickly on, *Enquire within upon Everything* hasn't got time to deal with doubters or uncertainty about do-it-yourself dentistry. After all, if you are giving advice about everything, there is only so much time you can afford to the relatively small problem of toothache:

> succedaneum – take an old silver thimble, an old silver coin, or other silver article, and with a very fine file convert it into filings. Sift through gauze, to separate the coarse from the fine particles. Take the finer portion, and mix with sufficient quicksilver to form a stiff amalgam, and while in this state, fill the cavities of decayed teeth.

Just in case anyone was beginning to have a few doubts, the writer breaks in with a note of assurance, as follows:

> this is precisely the same as the metallic amalgam used by all dentists. The filings of a sixpence would produce as much as is contained in two 2s 6d packets sold by the advertising makers of succedaneums. Quicksilver may be bought at a trifle per half ounce or ounce, at

the chemist's. We have not the slightest hesitation in pronouncing this to be the *best* thing of the kind.

Finally the whole section closes on a cosmetic issue, which sounds the only note of caution in the whole set of instructions:

> caution: as it turns black under the action of the acids of the mouth, it should be used sparingly for *front* teeth. A tooth should never be filled while it is aching.

After instructions like that, is it any wonder that people mad with pain chose to pull out bad teeth using the cotton and door method rather than subject themselves to teeth being filled with the residue from an old silver spoon.

Getting them out

Stories abound of people who used to have their teeth out whether they were damaged or not. One woman I know said that her mother had her teeth out for a twenty-first birthday present, the reason being that if they were removed, she wouldn't have any further trouble with them!

My own mother remembers having her teeth out, because of a gum disease which would be easily cured today. Her doctor came to the house and removed her teeth while she was lying drugged on the living room table. She says that she refused to think about the process before it took place and therefore hadn't put out any towels or cotton wool to staunch the wounds inflicted on her gums.

People do seem to have been incredibly stoic in the past. Catherine Ford says that her mother was in service in London to a very pleasant lady who looked after her well, apart from the occasion when she had her teeth out and was told to go straight back to work. Her sister Nellie, who lived in another part of London came to see her and was horrified. Nellie swept in, swept out again with her sister, and took her back to her house. The lady of the house wasn't being unkind, she just didn't think having all of one's teeth out was a major event. As a result of this Catherine's mother gave her some good advice along the lines of, 'hang on to your teeth as long as you can'.

Fish and chips

And finally, when I was pregnant, two teeth were found to be decayed so I had them fixed and covered with gold crowns as they were deemed to be very strong. Later I had them removed and two white crowns put in their place. The dentist gave me the gold crowns, which were huge. I passed them on to my young son who took them to the jewellers along the road. He weighed the crowns, then gave my son just enough money to buy fish and chips all round for supper that night.

Splinters

Do-it-yourself

For some unfathomable reason, splinters seem to have been more of an occupational hazard in days gone by. I suppose it had something to do with lifestyle and open fires. Today, many of us spend a fair amount of time in front of a computer, making a meal using gas or electricity, or driving around in cars. There are occupational hazards associated with computers, gas, electricity and cars, but they don't involve close contact with wood and the inevitable splinter.

Years ago, people were more inclined to make shelves, chop wood for the fire and play outdoors as children. Today we have the 'flatpack', where the closest you get to nature is choosing your shelf unit. We don't tend to have real fires any more, and children rarely, if ever, find time to play outdoors; they have so many computer games!

Granda Bianchi's first aid kit

At one time people always seemed to be getting splinters in their fingers. I remember my grandfather had a special eyeglass in his sideboard drawer, for the express purpose of getting splinters out of fingers. We would play in his garden, complete with dangers such as sheets of glass for the cold frame, a compost heap rotting away in the corner and even some bad tempered hens – and I'm not talking about my grandmother. I remember bursting in to the living room to tell him I'd got a splinter in my finger, and that it hurt like mad. The ritual of sterilising a sewing needle with boiling water would begin, then he would screw in his eyeglass and dig around for what seemed like hours until he captured the splinter and held it up for all to see. Everyone would marvel at the size of the splinter and the bravery I had shown in the face of such adversity.

Although the sharp needle hurt like mad, I remember feeling something close to enjoyment because a busy adult took time out from their day to concentrate on me and make me feel better. We didn't hold with fancy remedies in our family so after the surgical removal of the splinter I was advised to lick my wound and go out to play again. This time though I was warned to be a lot more careful and avoid sharp pieces of wood, as if for all the world I had done it deliberately!

Granda Bianchi's First Aid kit.

Basilicon Ointment – fanfare

My husband's mother was less inclined to dig around in her children's tender flesh with a needle and more inclined to recommend something called Basilicon Ointment. Indeed, this remedy was held in such esteem and affection in her house, that they referred to it as 'Basilican', a sort of nickname denoting a tried and trusted friend. When my children were little, she would recommend 'Basilican' for all sorts of skin ailments and I felt that I'd better get some of this magic potion just to be on the safe side. The trouble was that I never felt as confident as she did as regards its magical properties, so never used it, but kept it in the medicine cabinet as a sort of amulet against the dangers of splinters. She once tried explaining to me what it was used for and there was much talk about its drawing properties, but I sort of shut down at that point, as I didn't want to hear what was being drawn and how. I imagined that it involved blood, guts and pus!

Soap and sugar

Another friend, Jennifer Allen of Sunderland, has an auntie Dot, Sunday name, Dorothy Grieves, who remembers this particular remedy for fettling splinters. You had to wrap the offending finger in a plaster, which contained a mixture of soap, and sugar, and that would draw the splinter. I remember my own mother trying this remedy and can still feel the gritty sugar as it worked its way under my finger nail, and the clammy nature of the soap, clinging to my finger. Despite the discomfort, this particular remedy did manage to draw the splinter out of my finger.

Basilicon Ointment

The golden rule of pins

I didn't realise until I started talking to people about their splinter memories that their removal was such a hazardous affair. My sister's husband, born and brought up in London, remembers that his father used to remove splinters with a pin which had been heated on the gas stove to sterilise it. When my mother heard this she was astonished because she had been firmly instructed that you should always use a needle for removing splinters; regional differences coming to the fore again.

Poultices

Disgusting objects

On the subject of drawing things, look at the soggy subject of poultices.

Don't poultices sound disgusting? However they were offered as a remedy for all sorts of ancient ailments.

> *Got toothache?* What you need is a poultice.

> *Sore feet?* I think a poultice would do the trick here.

> *A sudden eruption of vile acne?* Hmmm I think a poultice might help.

> *Earache?* Yes, you've guessed it. A poultice wouldn't come amiss.

So that's that settled then, poultices were brilliant for everything. But let's get back to the knotty or rather soggy question of what constitutes a poultice? Well, they appear to have come in all shapes and sizes and were constituted from anything you could lay your hands on at that moment.

Good advice from 'Enquire within upon Everything'

Enquire within upon Everything, as expected, has this to say about poultices:

> poultices are usually made of linseed meal, oatmeal or bread, either combined with water or other fluids: sometimes they are made of carrots, charcoal, potatoes, yeast, and linseed meal, mustard etc, but the best and most common kind of poultice is a fabric made of sponge and wool felted together and backed by Indian rubber. It is called 'Markwick's Patent Songio-Piline'.

The method of using this poultice is as follows:

> a piece of the material of the required form and size is cut off, and the edges pared or bevelled off with a pair of scissors, so that the caoutchouc [Indian rubber] may come in contact with the surrounding skin, in order to prevent evaporation of the fluid used... The material costs about one farthing a square inch, and may be obtained from the chemist.

Brace Yourself!

Just in case there is any doubt about how to use the Songio-Piline, the book adds:

> full directions will, no doubt, be supplied to those who purchase the material, if inquired for.

Well, that's a relief, no more floundering about not knowing what to do with 'Marwicks Patent Songio-Piline'.

More exhausting detail

Enquire within upon Everything cannot let a good thing go, so proceeds with further detail on the damp subject of poultices. If you can't afford the 'Markwick's Patent Songio-Piline' there is no need to be unduly concerned. Although the 'Markwick's Patent Songio-Piline' has been heartily recommended only two lines previously, the little volume goes on to explain that the Patent Songio-Piline 'only forms the vehicle, so we can employ the various poultices with much less expenditure of time and money, and increased cleanliness'.

For example:

> a *vinegar* poultice is made by moistening the fabric with distilled vinegar;

> an *alum* poultice by using a strong solution of alum;

> a *yeast* poultice by using warmed yeast and moistening the fabric with hot water, which is to be well squeezed out;

a *beer* poultice by employing warm porter-dregs or strong beer as the fluid;

a *carrot* poultice can be made by using the expressed and evaporated liquor of boiled carrots; and

a *charcoal* poultice made by – yes, you're ahead of me on this one – sprinkling powdered charcoal on the moistened surface of the material.

As always in these cases, I am charmed by the use of italics – they give the instructions added weight somehow, and you don't like to imagine the consequences if you tried to make a poultice out of a turnip if you found you were clean out of carrots.

I also wonder how many people, when faced with a pint of strong beer, would instinctively think, 'hmm, better not have a drink, I think I'm going to be able to make a jolly good poultice out of this tomorrow'.

And finally, on the subject of poultices, I would pay good money to see someone wearing a charcoal poultice. Imagine going to work on the bus, buying a cup of coffee, booting up the computer, meeting people, and influencing them, all the while wearing a gently seeping black poultice.

Fashion and the changing poultice

The *New Home Encyclopaedia* edited by Joan Wheeler, and published by Odhams Press Ltd in London 1932, felt that poultices were a thing of the past and roundly declares:

fomentations are more handy and cleaner than poultices but do not keep the heat so long.

Similar to compresses, fomentations were generally used on the chest to break up colds and congestion but didn't retain the heat as well as poultices. The *Encyclopaedia* points out that fomentations 'involve towels, flannel, lint and boiling water'.

So, to be bang up to the minute you had to forget about charcoal poultices and move onto fomentations.

It's a wonder anyone ever survived a fomentation or a poultice. I bet you wouldn't be in too much of a hurry to admit that you might need one.

King George V and pleurisy

My mother, Lilian Bianchi, remembers, 'there used to be a horrible one [poultice] which was black stuff in a stick, which was heated and put on a bit of lint', and also remembered a 'kaolin poultice' which was for bad chests. Marion Coupe, a friend of my mother's remembers wearing a kaolin poultice for pleurisy, the poultice being put on a piece of linen and then wrapped round her side.

My mother also had pleurisy when she was about three years old, and her mother, Elizabeth Clark, bought a pleurisy jacket which she wore until she was better. This jacket was considered to be expensive but was the best remedy for pleurisy. Once worn, you couldn't just shed the jacket suddenly, the process had to be gradual. Consequently, every couple of days my grandmother would cut a little piece of the jacket off the main garment at the back and front, until finally there was very little jacket left and the patient was a healthy girl once more.

My mother remembers her doctor, Dr De Reddar, visiting her and confiding:

> you have a royal disease. King George himself has pleurisy and is convalescing in Bognor Regis at this very moment.

She was extremely impressed by this royal fact.

Romance and the poultice

Poultices do not, as a rule, feature in romantic stories. If anything, they are the antithesis of romance, but not in all cases. Audrey Ann Myers' parents met when her mother, Carol was fifteen years of age and her father, Len, was seventeen.

At one point her father got a bad cut on his hand which became septic. Her mother knew the very thing for the cut – no prizes for guessing – particularly as this story appears in the section about poultices. Yes, the solution was a poultice, in this case, a bread and butter poultice. It all sounded very interesting to me, after all, people with a lot of bread and butter on their hands usually end up making a bread and butter pudding, so I was intrigued to find out how this piece of home spun first-aid would work, and asked how it had gone. Audrey Ann's reply was terse, and went like this:

he was rushed to hospital, very ill, 'cos it didn't work!

Well, you can't win them all.

Colds, coughs and sore throats

Dr Haigh method

There are obviously whole books if not libraries to be written about colds, how to avoid getting them and how to treat them once you have succumbed to a cold's rheumy clutches. My Uncle John Piper said that a cold would disappear within seven days if it was treated and a week if it wasn't. I tend to subscribe to this theory and largely content myself with feeling very sorry for myself, soldiering on in the face of adversity, while spreading germs as far as I can.

My father was a strong believer in Doctor Haigh, which meant that he heralded the arrival of a cold by saying to my mother, 'Lily, I've got one of my usuals', then dosing himself liberally with whiskey and water. You could add in the optional extras of sugar or lemon juice but the whiskey was the essential ingredient. A friend's grandmother was very fond of the Doctor Haigh solution to the question of what do to with a cold, and on more than one occasion had to be helped up as she fell in the street. The gentleman delivering her home suggested that she shouldn't go out as she was obviously far from well. The family agreed with this diagnosis but secretly resolved to hide the whiskey bottle, when they realised that grandma wasn't so much ill from the cold as blind drunk from the remedy.

Sir Robert Bruce Lockhart (1886-1970), British author, diplomat, and journalist, was obviously of the same school of thought as my father for he suggests the following, quoted in the *Independent* (London, 25 Nov. 1989):

> as a cure for the cold, take your toddy to bed, put one bowler hat at the foot, and drink until you see two.

Guinness, whiskey or stout

Another friend, Bill Hearn, was brought up by his nana who was a strong advocate of treating colds with alcohol. She recommended the following:

> if you have a cold make a hot toddy, use whiskey, Guinness or stout – put the poker in the fire then plunge it into the alcohol.

I don't know why it was considered more effective to drink the alcohol hot. I reckon it was a bit more bother to achieve, therefore you could feel as if you were really going to some lengths to cure the cold and not just having a drink for the pleasure of it. Bill's nana used to add this rider to the cold cure remedy, 'you can't live a georgette life on a flannelette income', which is difficult to link closely to a cold remedy. Perhaps she was commenting on the fact that wealthy folks could solve their common cold problems with whiskey while those less well heeled could always resort to stout!

Every man's favourite cold remedy!

Sniff salt and hit the roof

Other home grown remedies for the common cold range from the sublime (whiskey) to the ridiculous. Dorothy Grieves remembers her grandmother as a formidable character. She and Dorothy's grandfather owned a jewellery shop and a furniture shop next door to each other in an area of South Shields known then as 'The Fad', (a pub in the area is still called by that name), but now more prosaically called Boldon Lane. Dorothy's grandmother suggested, nay insisted, that a cold would be helped along if you put some salt in your hand, wet it and sniffed it. It probably gave the onlookers a laugh and Dot said, 'God, you used to hit the roof when the salt went up your sore nose'.

Sweaty socks pressed into action

Another remedy that Dot remembers is, 'gargle with salt and water and drink soup'. The salt water soothes a sore throat whilst the soup aids fluid intake, and nourishes, both of which are vital in fighting a cold.

Today we still recommend hot drinks and soup, which help soothe and unblock airways.

A more bizarre and unorthodox suggestion that a sore throat was cured if you wrapped a sweaty sock round your neck. There must be some sound reason for this but even after consulting with several chemists I haven't come up with a likely explanation other than the person suggesting this remedy was having me on.

Parrish's Chemical Food

Yon Lawson, her of the cooked ear, has an auntie called Patricia Carr, who lives in Whitley Bay. She was a strong advocate of Parrish's Chemical Food to help you get through the winter and avoid coughs and colds. The whole thing sounds rather grim but she described it in a rather dreamy way – 'it was nice tasting, malty.'

Indeed, George Bernard Shaw, 1913 himself said 'you see, most people get well all right if they are careful and you give them a little sensible advice. And the medicine really did them good. Parrish's Chemical Food: phosphates, you know. One tablespoon to a twelve ounce bottle of water: nothing better, no matter what the case is'.

My mother remembers Parrish's Chemical Food as tasting strongly of iron and adds, 'if you were off colour it acted as a pick-me-up but I don't think it did your teeth any good'.

Another friend, Heather Morgan supports this theory for she says that her mother used to give her a wineglass full of Parrish's Chemical Food if she was under the weather. She had to drink it through a straw which was cut in half, for economy, and woe betide her if she let the Chemical Food touch the inside of her mouth. She was supposed to draw on the straw and direct the Chemical Food onto the back of her throat and then swallow – fast.

What doesn't kill you cures you!

Everything Within

We have a book at home with the shortened title of *Everything Within* published by Morrison and Gibb. PIts Sunday title is *News Chronicle*, presumably the name of the newspaper which was host to the all-encompassing volume, *Everything Within. A Library of Information for the Home* edited by A. C. Marshall.

The editor, in the foreword, states that the book is not meant to be an encyclopaedia but:

> its mission is to provide useful and dependable information on those phases of life that are linked indissolubly with the Home. Furthermore, *Everything Within* aims to be a Friend and counsellor in many thousands of homes.

The volume is given added weight via a frontispiece of His Most Excellent Majesty George VI recording his Christmas Day speech for the BBC. It was obviously bought by the great and the good as well as the humble poor, for easy reference in life's little trials, because our own copy of the book, which we picked up in a second hand bookshop, is signed by one-time broadcaster, Isabel Barnett.

Remedies for treating the common cold, in this royal volume, are a mixture of the familiar and the downright weird. For example, we are advised that the best warm drinks for this purpose are hot lemon squash or whiskey in hot water.

But this is followed by the advice to:

> steep the feet for five or ten minutes in hot water, as hot as can be born, to which have been added two tablespoons of mustard, while rubbing the sides of the nose *downwards* for ten minutes night and morning with lanoline.

I can see the benefit of using lanoline to eliminate a sore nose but the italic print of the word *downwards* leads me to wonder what on earth might happen if someone got confused and rubbed the sides of their noses upwards for ten minutes night and morning. Presumably the fate is too grisly to mention in this worthy book.

The writer then goes on to suggest various drugs of unusual origin and nature. He suggests that:

> for a feverish cold, with slight cough, ammoniated tincture of quinine …forms a popular and very useful remedy.

Tincture of quinine, although lethal in large doses, was used for the treatment of intermittent and remittent fevers.

The advice continues, and explores the cold/cough axis a bit more thoroughly.

> when there is quinsy, or rheumatic pain, salicylate of soda and phenacetin (10 grams of each may be taken). In all inflammation of the throat, oily applications, such as camphorated oil and a flannel bandage to the neck, do much good.

Flannel bandages – red, naturally

And there we have it, a flannel bandage. I thought it couldn't be long before the writer got round to mentioning the flannel bandage. Everyone I've spoken to while writing about old fashioned remedies, mentions flannel, and most of them go on to explain that the flannel had to be red.

According to Dorothy Grieves, there seemed to be mythical elements attached to the material in which you were wrapped. Her mother said it had to be red flannel, but she confesses that there were some differences of opinion in the household as her father believed in thermagene – a cotton wool impregnated with some worthy liniment.

Goose grease

Dougie Pincott, a Teesside poet, remembers his grandmother used to tell him to rub goose grease on his chest and back. He says his grandmother thought the smell of grease eased a sore chest. This may be quite likely or it may be more likely that rubbing your chest with any sort of grease generates some heat that eases the soreness. This theory sounds to me like a good one but I am never likely to try it due to the difficulties of getting your hands on goose grease. And once you did get it, who would be bold enough to rub your chest with it?

Jane's Receipt Book 1850

Dorothy Grieves owns the book of receipts and remedies, mentioned in the Introduction – Jane Catherine Barnsley's Receipt book January 8 1850. The book is a collection of recipes and remedies handwritten in beautiful copperplate writing by Jane, with a whole section on coughs and colds. Jane Catherine Barnsley was Dorothy's great, great grandmother and certainly kept a tidy house and a tight ship. Here are some of her remedies for coughs and colds.

Cough Mixture
1 penny worth Irish moss
1 penny worth essence of lemon
½ lb lump sugar

Sounds as if it might work but where would you lay your hands on Irish Moss today?

Naomi Jacobs cough mixture
6 oz syrup of squills
6 oz sweet spirit of nitre
6 oz toulou
6 oz paregoric

Mix, shake well. Dose – one large teaspoon either neat or in wineglass with hot water.

This remedy raises more questions than it answers, the main one being, 'who was Naomi Jacobs and why was she such an authority on cough mixture?' I bet she was Jane's aunt or her mother's friend who over the years had gained a reputation for fettling coughs almost before they'd even begun.

Or what about this one

  1 gill black beer
  1 gill vinegar
  ½ lb black treacle
  ½ lb brown sugar

  Boil all together for 20 minutes. When cold add ½ gill
  rum. Bottle and take a good teaspoonful three times a day.

I like the sound of it better than Naomi Jacobs but I hope no-
one who took it was driving a bus that day or operating heavy
machinery. The amount of alcohol in that recipe would make
it the highlight of any cocktail party… so long as they went
easy on the vinegar!

Colds & 'Flu

so often start with a sore throat

Beware the raw, tickling throat which precedes a cold or 'flu. That is your signal to take Cephos and stop the attack immediately. It does not affect the heart.

Cephos
THE PHYSICIANS' REMEDY

SOLD EVERYWHERE in tablet or powder form.
1/3 & 3/-

Single dose 2d.

Advert for Cephos Colds and Flu Remedy 1943

Chilblains

Chill what?

Ask anyone over the age of 50 what a chilblain is and chances are they'll not know precisely but remember their aunties and nanas suffering with them. Ask anyone over the age of seventy and they will probably remember some member of their family suffering cruelly with chilblains. Ask anyone under the age of 50 about chilblains and they will simply look blank. What were they? What did they look like? What caused them? And how did you get rid of them?

Soothing advice from 'Everybody's Family Doctor'

Everybody's Family Doctor soothingly takes the mystery out of chilblains. It starts off by saying that:

> the disease is only too well known, occurs during the winter months only and is found especially in children who are below par.

The book then goes on to explain that chilblains are all to do with poor circulation, thin clothes and underfeeding, tight boots and gloves and the too rapid warming of your hands. Blimey – you must have had to be on red alert the whole time if you wanted to avoid chilblains. Treatment was fairly rigorous too and could be conducted along the lines of 'general, local and preventative'. The sufferer had to improve circulation by taking cod liver oil and tonics like Easton's syrup and Fowler's solution, treat itching via calamine lotion or iodine, but not too much iodine otherwise you would be subject to 'iodine itching', and as a last resort, hot air baths and X-rays were recommended as being very useful, along with 'electric treatment by the high-frequency current'. The handy watchword, according to *Everybody's Family Doctor* was:

> prepare in summer for the winter…in other words, preventative treatment must not be given up as soon as the winter's crop of chilblains disappear.

Poultices again and Elizabeth I

Enquire within upon Everything also takes chilblains seriously, and advocates using a poultice of bread and water on ulcers 'for a day or two' and then dressing with something called 'calamine cerate or…by an extract of lead used pure or applied on lint twice a day'. Now, don't get me wrong, I'm sure the authoritative volume contains a lot of good stuff, but wasn't it lead which completely destroyed the face of Elizabeth I? And she simply painted it on her face once a day. This book of handy household hints has got its readers applying lead twice a day!

Wear ugly boots

Chilblains then, were no laughing matter. It was important not to get them in the first place, for, as *News Chronicle – Everything Within* stated, the least little thing could bring them on. Tight boots, or warming the hands by the fire was enough to engorge the blood vessels and lead to chilblains. The book further suggested that:

> regular exercise and a cold bath every day improve the circulation...the person liable to chilblains should wear wide boots, and thick woollen socks in winter. Garters should be abolished and hands and feet never held in front of the fire for warmth.

So not only did you feel terrible, with itching hands and feet and the knowledge that you should have a cold bath, you also looked terrible, wearing thick socks and unfashionable boots.

Wintergreen

My mother remembers getting lots of chilblains, on the back of her heels and on her fingers. The problem suddenly stopped after she became pregnant but before then she used a remedy called 'Wintergreen' which came in a tiny tin box, cost about three pence and which was put beside the open fire to melt before being spread on the chilblains. She also says that she wore half finger gloves in the office, in an effort to keep her circulation moving. No central heating then, just lots of people wearing gloves to keep warm at work.

Beware of fires

Bill Hearn's nana had this advice, 'don't stand in front of the fire when its cold, you'll take all the marrow out of your bones' which seems odd at first but on mature reflection it combines the internal and external protection systems judged to be necessary for combating chilblains. His nana may not have known much about the theory of medicine, but she did know that extremes of heat caused the circulation to go mad and lead to chilblains, and that internally, they could be prevented by good food and tonics, all designed to increase calcium and build strong bones.

On a slightly different note, obviously anything that you enjoy is always bad for you, so the fire, probably our greatest home-based pleasure before the advent of television, was clearly bad for you. I remember my mother telling me that when she and my father were first married they would cuddle up and gaze into the open fire to see what pictures appeared. Open fires are still seductive, that's why we all buy gas fires that have 'living flames'. Most of the heat goes up the chimney but we love them, because they look just like the real thing, and give you a feeling of home, belonging, relaxation and comfort.

Cinder legs

Ladies used to be warned not to sit in front of the fire, because of the dire consequences. I remember a lovely woman who used to go to my church, 'The People's Mission' at the Lawe Top, South Shields, when I was a little girl, who sat for too long in front of the fire, and illustrated the problem graphically.

She was a great pianist and good at sewing, so each year, at church, when the Christmas play was mooted, she would get the job of making some of the costumes. On one occasion I was the chief angel, which meant that I had to have wings with a bigger wingspan than the other angels. This was really a feat of engineering rather than dressmaking, and it necessitated several visits to this lady's home for fittings. I don't think I've ever had a dress that took longer to fit but once it was done, those wings felt as if they were part of me. Anyway what fascinated me were the lady's legs. They were purple and red at the front and flesh coloured at the back. I asked several people recently what they made of the troubled topic of the red and blue legs, and reached this conclusion.

I reckon it was because people used to sit practically on the fire to keep warm. Older folk who can remember what it was like before central heating say that you had to huddle over the fire with one side of your body slowly roasting and the other side subject to the icy blasts swooshing up the back stairs. Ruth Hearn remembers her grandmother giving her the advice, 'don't sit in front of the fire for too long or your shins will get cinders.'

'Cinders' must have been the word used to describe shins mottled like a map of Europe before the dissolution of the Commonwealth, all red and gorgeous blue.

Legs red and gorgeous blue like a map of the Empire.

The inner self

Spring medicine and spots

When I was a young girl, and it was particularly important to look good, I would erupt in a rash of spots and pimples, which caused me to be furiously angry. I was angry if my mother mentioned the spots and angry if she didn't. Angry if she called them spots and furious if she called them pimples. She couldn't win, so she used to take solace in making me something called 'Spring Medicine' designed, so she said, 'to cool the blood'. Nowadays we don't hear much about cooling the blood, presumably the blood doesn't heat up the way it used to; but then, cooling the blood was obviously of huge significance.

The Spring Medicine Recipe belonged to my granny and she inherited it from her mother so it probably dates back to the 1850s. My grandmother, Elizabeth Clark, made the medicine in a white jug decorated with green ivy leaves. She then placed a saucer on top and a little glass on top of that. You had a glass of it every morning and my mother says:

> you were supposed to stir it up before you poured because the Epsom salts would sink to the bottom. But we didn't, we just used to have the lemon drink.

The whole thing was obviously a purgative and my mother confides, 'they were great on laxatives in those days'.

Here then is the Spring Medicine Recipe.

Spring Medicine
6 lemons, sliced
6 oz Epsom salts
6 oz granulated sugar
2 pts boiling water

Jane Catherine Barnsley's Receipt book January 8 1850 includes a recipe for Fruit Salts.

Fruit Salts
3 oz Tartaric Acid
2 oz best Epsom Salts
2 oz carbonate soda
3 oz cream of tartar
18 oz lump sugar grounded

My mother doesn't think much of it. She likes her own recipe best and thinks that the Barnsley version is much too high on the salts and totally lacking in the fruit department.

Incidentally, you probably had to be reasonably alert when following recipes, as the Fruit Salts recipe in Jane's book, is closely followed by:

Varnish for furniture
1 gill spirit of wine
3 oz shellac
1½ Venetian Red mixed with thin glue water

You could end up totally purged but feeling a bit wooden.

Brimstone and treacle

Enquire within upon Everything that bombastic little volume, has this to say, 'in the spring time of the year, the judicious use of aperient medicine is much to be commended', and goes on to give a recipe which sounds ferocious in design and frenzied in application.

Here goes:

> for children – Brimstone and Treacle prepared by mixing an ounce and a half of sulphur and a half an ounce of cream of tartar with eight ounces of treacle, and according to the age of the child giving from a small teaspoonful to a dessert spoonful early in the morning two or three times a week. As this sometimes produces sickness the following may be used.
>
> One drachm and a half of powdered Rochelle salts, of powdered jalap and rhubarb fifteen grains, of ginger two grains. Mix. An adult should take three teaspoonfuls. This medicine may be dissolved in warm water, mint or common tea. The powder can be kept for use in a wide mouthed bottle and be in readiness for any emergency. The druggist may be directed to treble or quadruple the quantities as convenient.

Syrup of Figs

Syrup of Figs sounds lovely, but believe me, tasted vile. The *Sunday Pictorial* of 1 November 1942 contains a cheery picture of a mother holding her little girl. The girl is smiling broadly while gently patting the mother's face. This was obviously a 'before' rather than an 'after' Syrup of Figs picture.

The text is similarly upbeat, 'Children love the pleasant taste of California Syrup of Figs brand laxative, and gladly take it even when bilious, feverish, sick or constipated. No other laxative regulates the tender little bowels so nicely. It sweetens the stomach and stimulates the liver without cramping or over-acting. Millions of mothers depend on this gentle harmless laxative. Tell your chemist you want California Syrup of Figs. Mother, you must say 'CALIFORNIA'.'

The copywriters obviously felt that the use of the word 'California' was a winner, denoting sunshine, wholesome living, and presumably, healthy bowel action.

Worm cakes

Constipation wasn't the only worry for mothers, for, whisper it softly, some children got worms, and there's nothing beautiful about the inner self if it is inhabited by worms. Worm cakes could be bought at the chemist. They sound like cakes made out of worms, but must have been a cake to get rid of the little blighters.

Linda Giles has an interesting remedy for sorting out worms. She advises, 'If you have a tape worm, you should starve yourself, then fry bacon and the tape worm would pop out of your mouth.' I thought this advice sounded barmy, but Catherine Ford, who was listening to this conversation, nodded wisely and added the information that her mother reckoned 'You had to tempt them out'. This conjures up the image of a harassed mother frying bacon and performing the dance of the seven veils while dressed as Salome. And all before breakfast.

Warts and boils

What rot!

Like splinters, warts were once seen as part of growing up, and most children came complete with three or four warts on their fingers. Theories about warts were almost as prolific as the warts themselves. Remedies and old wives tales abound.

My father was never a very superstitious man, but he remembered his mother, Elizabeth Bianchi, getting rid of his warts some time in the 1930s, by the simple method of burying pieces of string in the garden. She asked him how many warts he had, cut the corresponding pieces of string, buried them in the garden at the dead of night, and said nothing. This 'said nothing' bit was obviously the magic touch that did it, because as the string started to rot in the ground, so the warts on my dad's hand also started to rot and disintegrate. He was fairly sceptical about luck, magic, old wives tales and the like, but retained a simple faith in the healing properties of burying bits of string in a garden.

Carnivorous remedy

My father's mother obviously favoured the vegetarian method of getting rid of warts, i.e., using pieces of string rather than something which was once alive. However, after talking to people about the string method of dealing with the little fellas, I have uncovered a remedy using meat. Obviously this method is dependant on the fact that you could afford to buy meat and then let it rot in the ground. Not an option for everyone.

The meat method is as follows, count up the number of warts you have on your hands, cut a lump of meat into a corresponding number of pieces, then bury the pieces of meat in the ground, and as the meat rots so the warts will rot.

Alan Sigsworth, who used to live in the north east of England but now isn't so fortunate, can also add detail to the carnivorous method of dealing with warts. He remembers a remedy that suggested you put a piece of steak into a matchbox and then bury the whole thing in the garden. That way, you could be sure that your warts would rot.

Other people swear that this method only succeeds if you first rub the offending warts with the separate pieces of meat before burying them in the ground.

A match

Ruth Hearn's mother swore by the following remedy as a cure for warts. She would wet a match and paint the offending area with the damp red phosphorus. *Enquire within upon Everything*, in a section airily entitled, 'Poisons, General Observations' treats phosphorus with respect, recommending that if it is swallowed, you should 'take large draughts of cold water and tickle the throat with a feather'.

Buying warts in Lincoln

A friend who was brought up in Lincoln was quite stirred by these remedies regarding warts and tried to find out a bit of family folklore on general aliments and warts in particular. He seems to have struck a strong vein of scepticism in his family because after digging around for a while, he responded as follows:

> your book sounds fascinating and I'm asking around the family for old Lincolnshire remedies. Sadly all our remedies came from the chemist or a brandy bottle, though my mother would 'buy' my warts from me (ten bob a wart I think). It didn't work.

Other remedies were more brutal, and I remember the school nurse, circa 1959, burning off a couple of warts on my fingers with a caustic solution, which caused me to lose all feeling in the offending fingers. The nurse was able to scrape away, occasionally drawing blood, while I watched and laughed as merry as a cricket.

Warts and all!

The evil eye method

Alan Sigsworth remembers a rather unusual remedy for getting rid of warts, which involved Sammy Darke, the chemist, who used to have a reputation as an unorthodox type of healer.

This unorthodoxy extended to strange sounding ingredients. For example, Alan remembers once being sent by his uncle Tom, to buy two pen'orth of 'appadildock' and some 'harts horn'. Alan knew that the nearest chemist, Darlings, would be no help on this occasion, because Darlings were regarded as a chemist of the modern era while Sammy's shop in Frederick Street, South Shields, had a reputation for knowing more about traditional remedies, and further more, being prepared to try them out. The recipe, which seems to have been the basis for smelling salts, was odd to say the least. 'Harts horn' was apparently originally ground from the horns or hooves of animals, and is more commonly referred to as baking ammonia, whereas appadildock is a kind of creamy soap type substance.

Alan knew that Darke's would have all of the odd ingredients and also know what to do with them.

Sammy Darke, in addition to knowing about strange ingredients, was supposed to have 'the eye'. Folks would take themselves off to see Sammy with their warts. He would then, according to tradition, give the warts 'the eye' and the warts disappeared. Magic, or the power of suggestion? Who knows and who cared? So long as your warts disappeared, you wouldn't be too fussy.

The needlework method

As usual in the past, our ancestors displayed a casual and relaxed nature to removing bits of the body that weren't absolutely essential. Warts, being regarded as 'small harmless tumours of the skin' according to *Everybody's Family Doctor* were due to an infection and had to be removed. The writer advocates:

> 'the simplest method of treatment is to freeze the warts with ethyl chloride and snip them off with scissors: or they may be destroyed by freezing with carbon dioxide snow.'

The needlework method is the one that is strongly recommended as it may hurt, but it will be over quickest. However, if you were of a delicate constitution, you could try 'caustic, such as salicylic or acetic acids' which are 'efficient but slow, and the pain naturally lasts over a longer period'.

The reader is left in no doubt which method is preferred.

X-rays

Everybody's Family Doctor continues with some remarkable advice, given what we know today about X-rays, and the fact that in films, everyone always darts out of the room as soon as an X-ray is even mentioned. This then is the suggestion:

the effect of X-rays on warts is, in careful hands, remarkable, large crops often disappearing in a very short time.

but the writer then warns casually:

on the other hand, in some cases, this treatment may fail entirely.

Well, you can't say you weren't warned.

Poison

Finally then, and most alarmingly, *Everybody's Family Doctor* advises people with warts to drink poison:

internally, arsenic in small doses, Epsom salts, or green iodine of mercury will sometimes produce a cure: and the injection of salvarsan (an arsenic preparation) is successful in some cases.

Bear in mind that this advice could be found in a manual designed for the general public. The Introduction states:

the purpose of this book is a practical one... it is hoped that this work will not only prove of great practical value and interest in times of sickness, but will also serve as a helpful guide to the best ways of maintaining the health of the individual.

I thank my lucky stars daily that my mother saw fit to take me to the clinic for wart treatment rather than take it into her head to follow the advice of *Everybody's Family Doctor* and start dosing me with arsenic.

Don't believe all you read!

Things we'd never do now

Blazing fires

At one time fires were central to a home with everyone congregating around a roaring blaze.

I remember my grandfather making me a little three legged stool, called a cracket – the name now seems unlikely, and I wondered if I'd made it up. However people reassured me that crackets were once very much part of northern family life, along with proggy mats. Anyway, I arrived, aged about four years old, at my grandparents house and they presented me with a little cracket whose legs were only the tiniest bit uneven. I sat on it in front of the fire, and to everyone's surprise, proceeded to tumble into the fire. I managed to save myself from having a really nasty accident, as opposed to only a nasty accident, by putting out my hands and clinging to the metal grate containing the live coals.

Everyone panicked a bit then my nana rushed me to the kitchen and plunged my hands into a jar of flour. I can still remember the cool feeling of the flour on my hot burned hands.

You'd think that that sort of accident would be unusual, but not a bit of it. My friend Jennifer Allen's Auntie, Dorothy Grieves, whose ancestor wrote the Recipe Book of 1850, remembers a time when Jennifer's father was ill, her mother had to look after him, so Jennifer was sent to visit her aunt. Dot remembers Jennifer falling into the hearth, and burning her arm on the fire.

Its no wonder that remedies for dealing with burns were plentiful and elaborate. Today we are advised to run cold water over a burn then cover it with a sterile cloth. However, in the past, everyone had a view and every view was different. People were, and remain, sharply divided about the best way of treating burns.

Tannic acid and medicated paraffin

Everybody's Family Doctor has a bit to say on the subject, not all of which is very enlightening, but there are substantial detailed instructions which must have been a comfort. They read as follows:

> the best treatment is to spray on a 2% solution of tannic acid in warm water; the tannic acid coagulates the surface and prevents the absorption of poisons.

If you can't get your hands on solution of tannic acid, however, don't despair, you can always use 'medicated paraffin (ambrine) and 1% piric acid solution in hot water'. That's a comfort. Even if you haven't got a ready stock of tannic acid, you are bound to have some medicated paraffin or piric acid hanging about. Aren't you?

Dry, wet or oily

News chronicle – Everything Within has this to add:

slight burns are soothed by applying soap or spirit or by running tepid water over the burnt part.

and then advocates one of three methods:

Dry dressing – the burn may be thickly powdered with a dusting powder of starch and boracic acid in equal parts, and thereafter wrapped in cotton wool.

Wet Dressing – wrap the burnt area in strips of lint wrung out of warm boracic lotion or water with a little tincture of iodine, maintained at body temperature.

And finally, oily dressings made of carron oil which contains limewater and linseed oil in equal parts, with a certain amount of eucalyptus oil for its antiseptic properties.

The remedies outlined above presume that everyone had a fully stocked medicine cupboard, and aeons of time at their disposal. All well and good I hear you say, but isn't there something missing? Of course. Where is the remedy which recommends the use of alcohol? There can be very few situations when a homespun remedy does not advocate drinking, or rubbing on, or gargling with some form of alcohol. As usual, *Enquire within upon Everything* does not let us down.

Brandy and laudanum anyone?

The book suggests the following:

of all the applications for a burn, we believe there are none equal to the simple covering of common wheat flour. This is always at hand and while it requires no skill in using, it produces most astonishing results. The moisture produced upon the surface of a slight burn is absorbed by the flour and forms a paste which shuts out the air. It can also be readily washed off very carefully when it has become matted and dry and a new covering sprinkled on.

Enquire within upon Everything goes on with another much more elaborate remedy:

> take chalk and linseed, or common oil and mix them in such proportions as will produce a compound as thick as thin honey; then add vinegar so as to reduce it to the thickness of treacle; apply with a soft brush or feather, and renew the application from time to time. Each renewal brings fresh relief. If the injury is severe, give ten drops of laudanum to an adult, and repeat it in an hour and again a third time. To a child of ten years give only three drops; and beware of giving any to infants. This plan, with an internal stimulant, according to age, as brandy or sal volatile, or both, should be at once adopted, until the arrival of the medical attendant.

That's brandy, laudanum and sal volatile. I bet doctors and nurses witnessed people in rare states, and heard some bizarre tales!

Juggling with hot coals

The number of minor accidents involving burns must have been huge but people seemed to have been much hardier fifty years ago. I remember gazing in astonishment as my grandmother, Elizabeth Clark, tidied up the hearth by picking up live coals with her bare hands and throwing them back into the fire.

Juggling with hot coals!

Conclusion

I could go on all night. I haven't even touched upon remedies for morning sickness, remedies on how to have a comfortable delivery – of a baby of course. I haven't talked about remedies for white hands or tight curls, and believe me, I've got some corkers. All that will have to wait for another time. Meanwhile, I've enjoyed writing this random history of how we survive and I hope you enjoyed reading it.

Bibliography

Barnsley's, J. C. (ed) (1850), *Receipt Book,* Tyne & Wear.

Marshall, A. C. (ed), *News Chronicle – Everything Within. A Library of Information for the Home.*

Wheeler, J. (ed) (1932), *The New Home Encyclopaedia.* Long Acre, London. Odhams Press Ltd.

Enquire within upon Everything. Paternoster Square, London. Houlston and Sons.

Everybody's Family Doctor. Harley Street, London. Odhams Press Ltd.